I Read

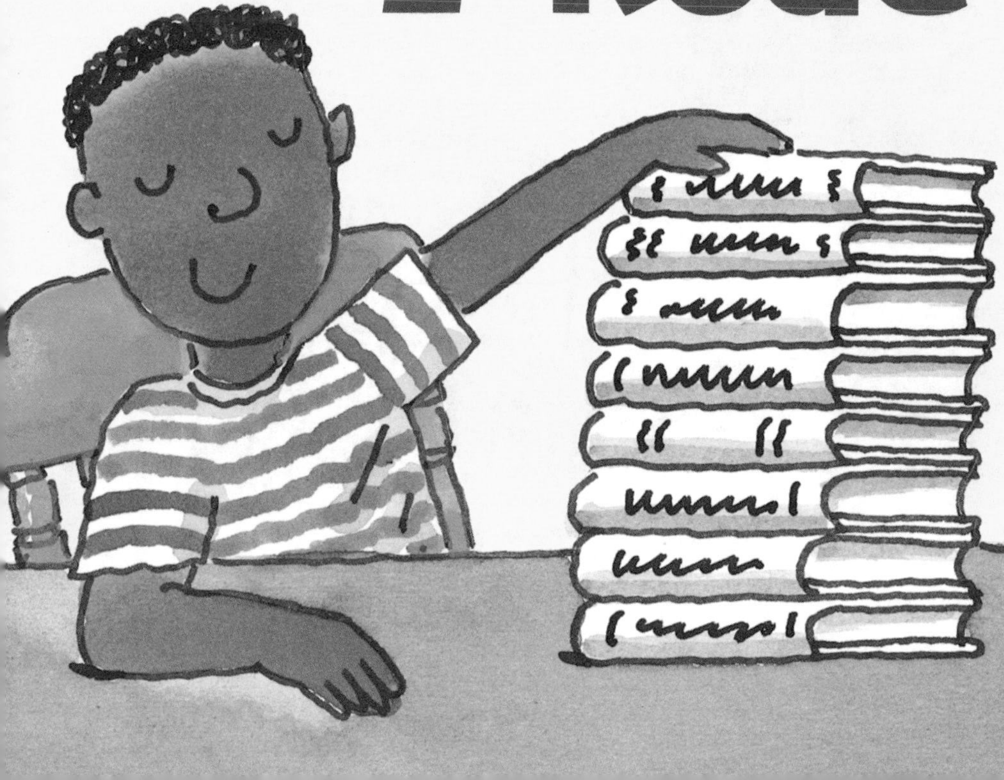

1

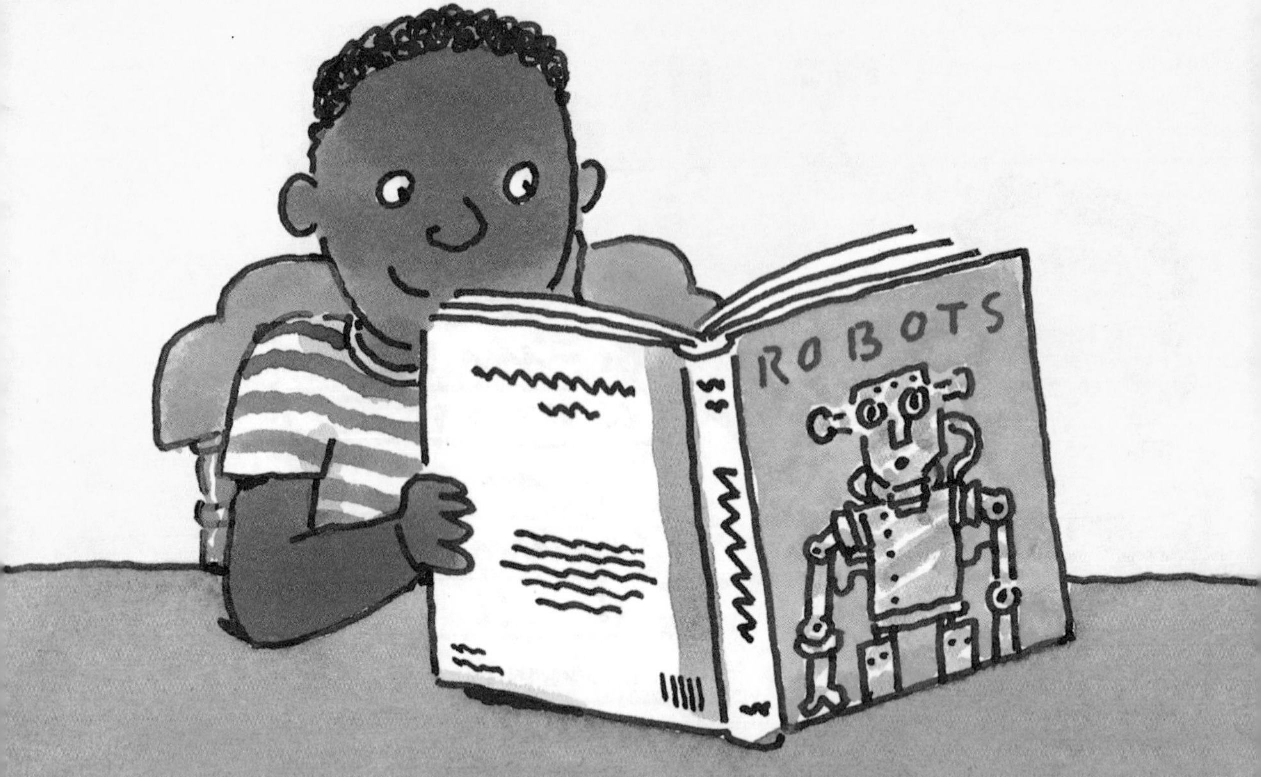

I read about robots.

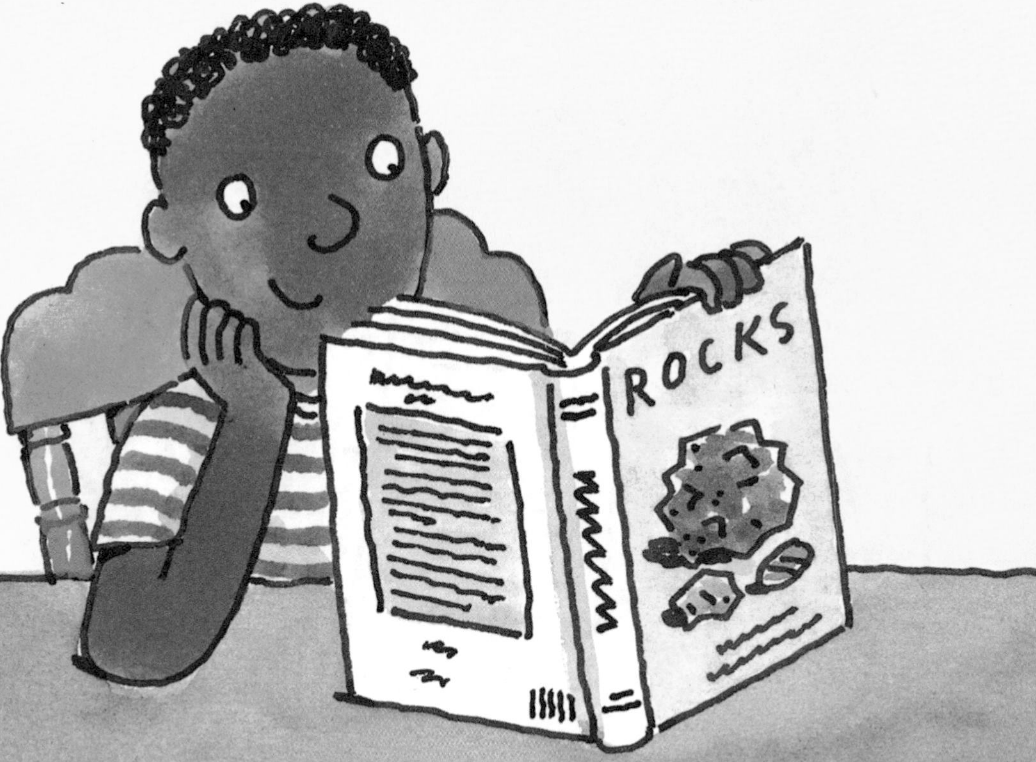

I read about rocks.

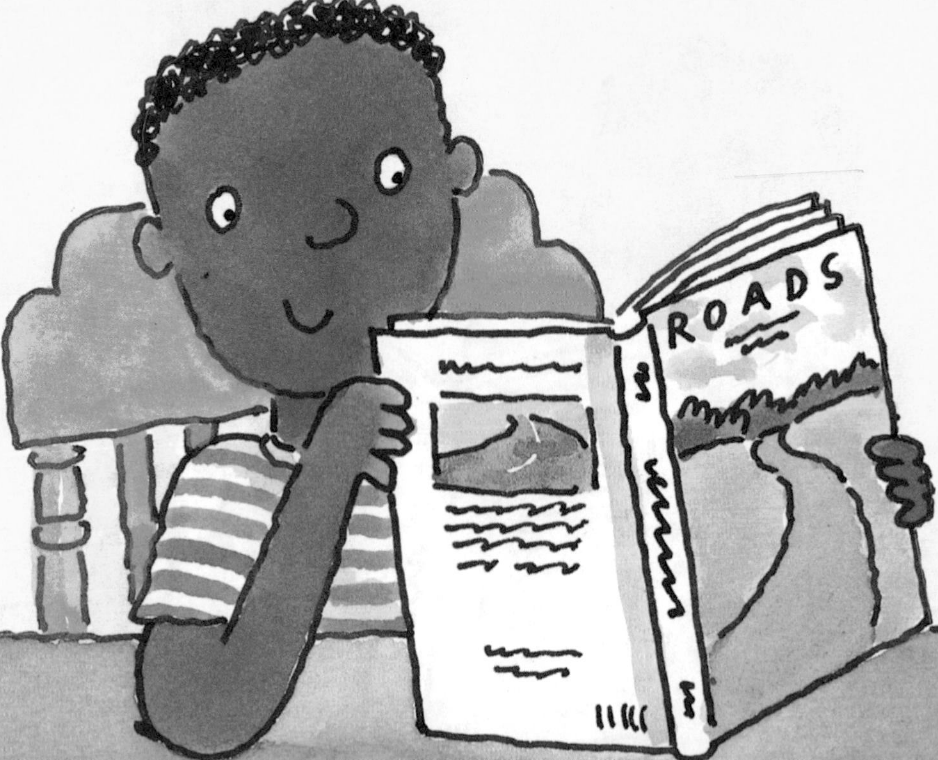

I read about roads.

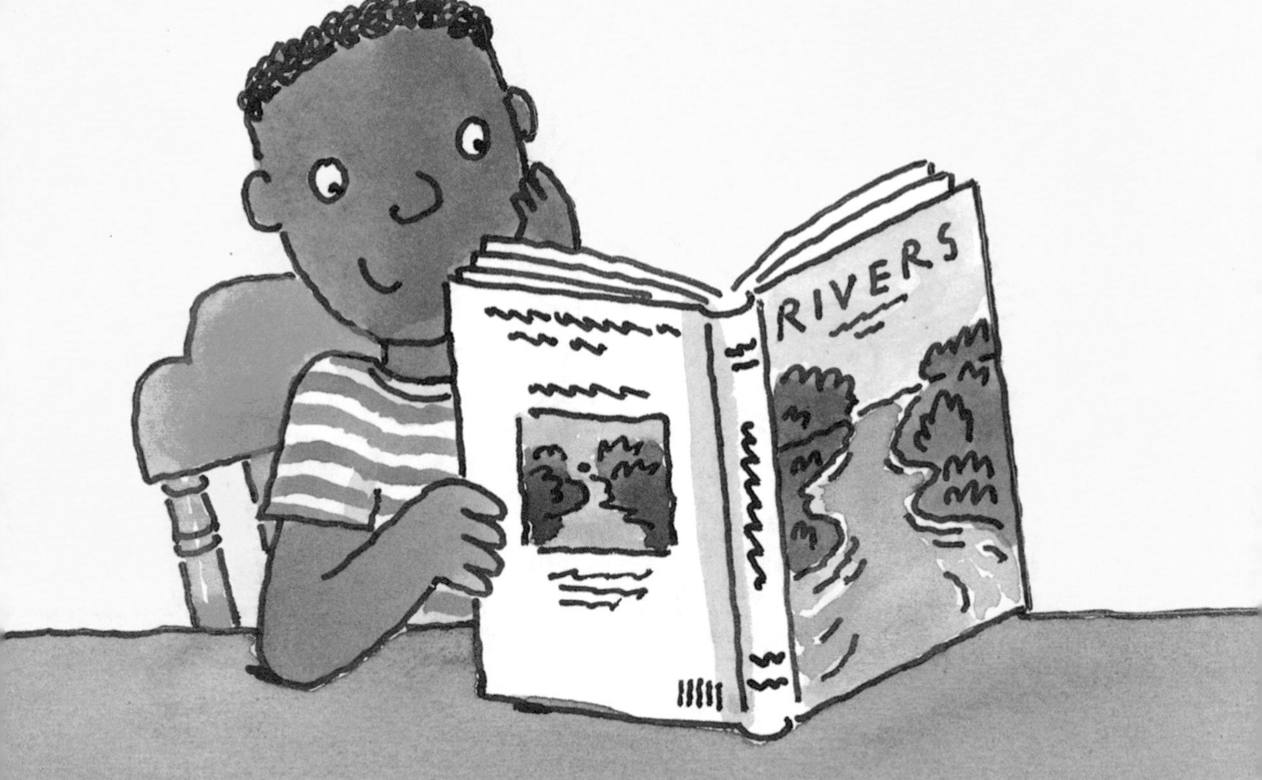

I read about rivers.

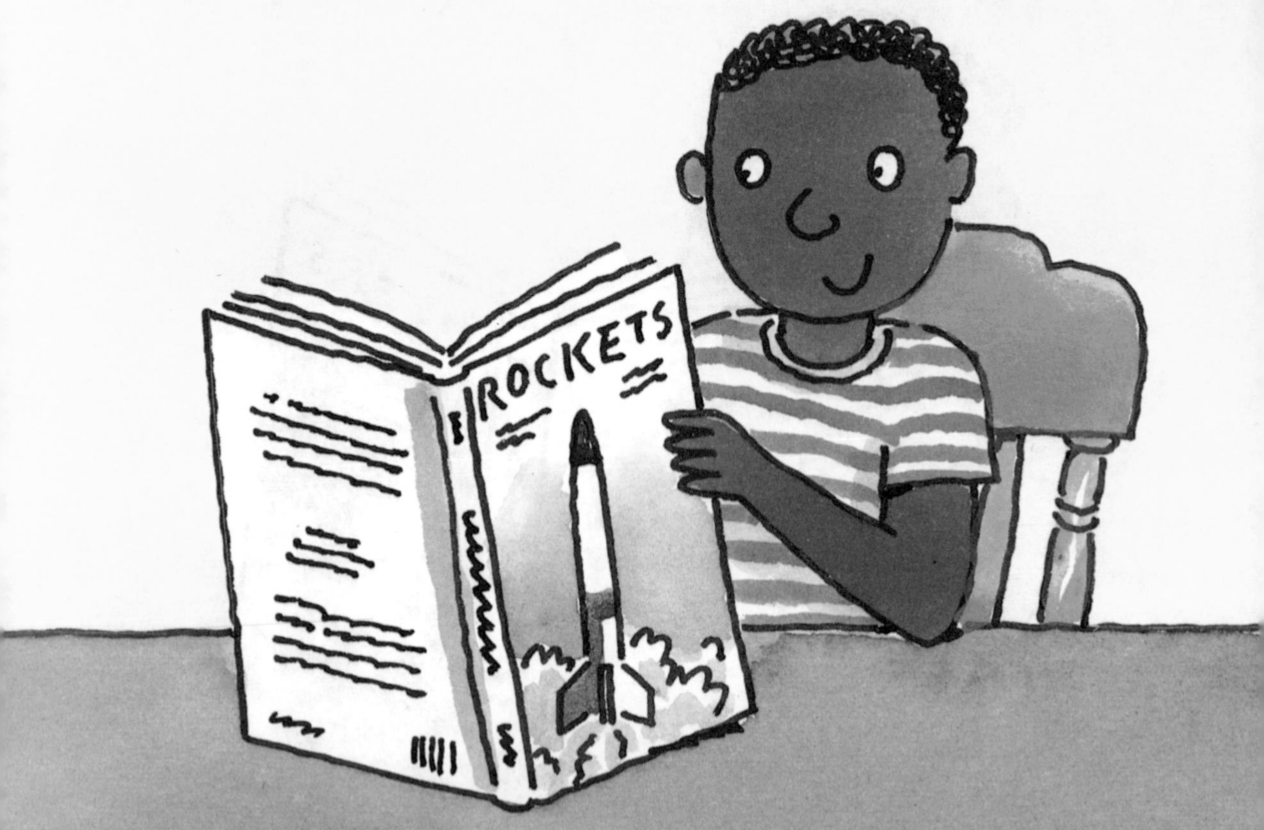

I read about rockets.

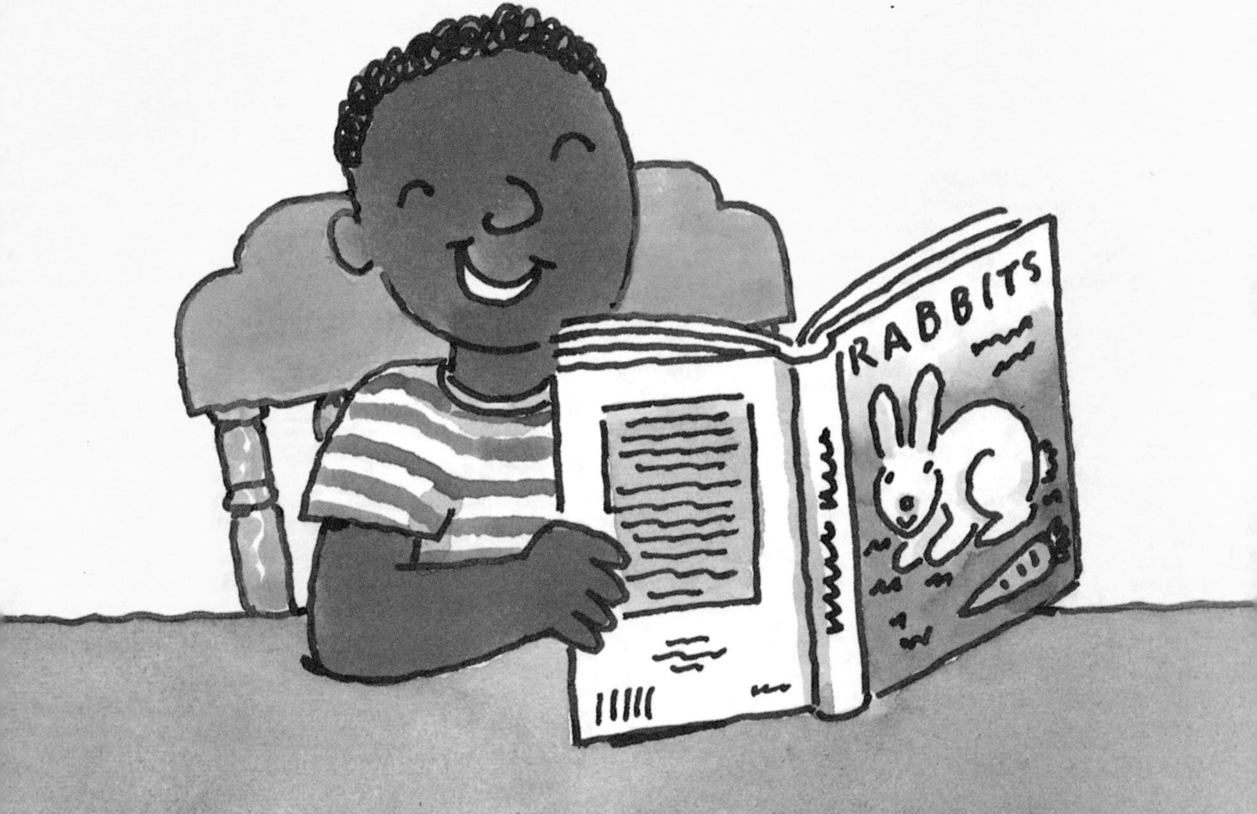

I read about rabbits.

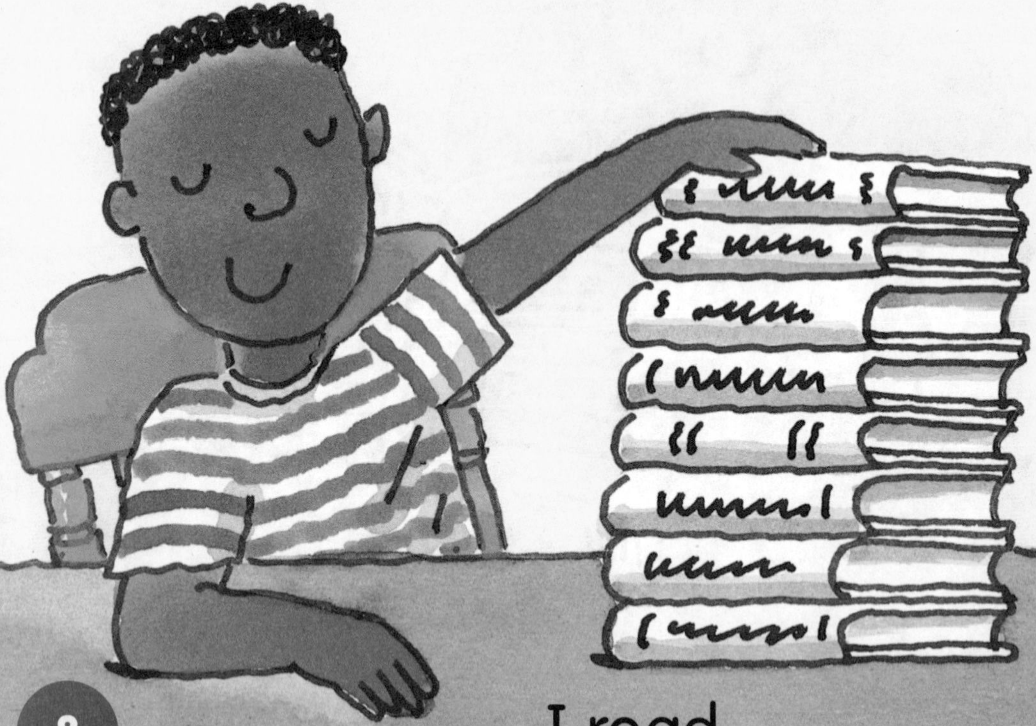

I read.